NOTHING IS IMPOSSIBLE

NOTHING IS IMPOSSIBLE

by

MERCEDES BALLESTEROS

TRANSLATED BY FRANCES PARTRIDGE

LONDON

THE HARVILL PRESS

Published by
THE HARVILL PRESS LTD
23 Lower Belgrave Street
London: S.W.1
1956

Printed in Great Britain by
BUTLER & TANNER LTD
Frome, Somerset

TO MY DAUGHTER
VERONICA

PEOPLE used to say that little Andrés never stopped dreaming even when he was awake, but the truth of the matter was that he was never really awake at all. He was like someone walking through a cloud, in which anything, however extraordinary, might happen.

In this secret world of his there lived a certain Livia Aivil, whose name was the same whether it was read backwards or forwards; so that Livia Aivil was the embodiment of infinity, for she ended where she began, and began again where she ended, and so on and on for ever. She was no sooner there than she was gone again, as if she had disappeared on purpose to make room for a sylph called Carlota Pelín, who was very small and round as a cheese.

'But sylphs are never small and plump like Carlota Pelín,' someone said.

'It doesn't matter,' replied little Andrés. 'She is a sylph all the same, a sylph as round and white as a cheese.'

7

Andrés was at the top of his class, as a result of the end-of-term examinations, in which he had done brilliantly and got the highest marks. This was a mystery. Or rather it was one more mystery. For everything to do with little Andrés was strange and inexplicable.

'It isn't fair,' said Francisco angrily. 'It isn't fair, because he was helped by Santa Margarita Maria de Alacoque. She does whatever he wants her to. I've seen it myself.'

This was a very serious accusation, and soon a good many other boys sided with Francisco and went to see the Headmaster, to complain that little Andrés had been in secret communication with the Saint.

But the Headmaster refused to consider the charge. He had had quite enough complaints. What with the endless grumblings of mothers and pupils about the heating of the school being inadequate, or about this or that, he really couldn't be bothered with an accusation against one of the boys for satisfying the examiners by means of miracles.

'Things like that don't happen in this prosaic, wicked world of ours.'

'However wicked the world is,' Francisco still argued, 'I promise you that what I say about little Andrés really is true. I've seen it.'

'What have you seen?'

'I've seen him talking to Santa Margarita Maria de Alacoque in the Chapel.'

'Well, and what were they talking about?'

'Can't you guess, sir?'

'I never guess!'

'He was asking her to tell him the answers to the questions in his exam. Otherwise how could little Andrés, who never does any work at all, possibly have answered all the questions without making one single mistake?'

'All right then, what do you want me to do? Lock him up? Or lock up Santa Margarita Maria de Alacoque?'

The deputation of schoolboys had not thought of this last possibility, but when they heard it from the lips of their Headmaster they greatly approved of it.

Francisco said, voicing the wishes of the rest: 'We insist that Santa Margarita Maria de Alacoque be expelled from the school. She must understand that she is not allowed to meddle in our affairs.'

Thereupon the Headmaster brought his fist down on the table so violently that he sent flying a large pile of examination papers, which none of the boys would stoop to pick up, so angry were they.

'All very fine! And next time you'll insist that San Luis Gonzago be forced to leave the Chapel, and . . .'

'Oh no,' interrupted Francisco, 'San Luis Gonzago is innocent.'

'Silence!' shouted the Headmaster. 'No one can succeed in his exams without working!'

'But this wasn't working, it was cheating.'

'Do you know what you're saying? You dare to accuse Santa Margarita Maria de Alacoque of cheating?'

The door opened and someone came in. Someone who was not so heated as the others in the room, someone who looked serene and meek.

'May I come in, sir?'

'I don't know why you ask, since you're in already.'

'I'm sorry, sir,' piped little Andrés in his treble voice. 'I did knock, but no one answered.'

'Very well, what do you want?'

'I know that the other boys have come to complain of me.'

At this a small uproar broke out. Francisco, Juan and Jorge all spoke at once. They repeated their accusation with heat. Andrés listened attentively without trying to interrupt. When they had finished he took several steps forward and stood before the Headmaster's table.

'It's true,' he said soberly. 'Santa Margarita Maria de Alacoque did tell me, one by one, all the answers to the questions I was to be asked.'

For a few moments the hullabaloo was such that not a single word could be heard. The Headmaster tried to restore order but without success. At last he managed to make himself heard, by shouting at the top of his voice:

'Get out, all of you! Get out, everyone but Andrés!'

When he was alone with the accused he looked him straight in the face.

'Do you still stick to what you said?'

'Yes, sir.'

'Do you expect anyone to believe you?'

'I don't know, sir.'

There was a pause.

Then the Headmaster said: 'Look. Supposing it *were* true. I mean . . . supposing that you imagine you heard what you've told us, don't you see how foolish it was to blurt it out like that? Don't you realize that by doing so you gave those lunatics an excuse for their behaviour?'

'Yes; I do see what you mean, sir. And I see what an idiot I am; but I'm not a liar.'

II

THE school post was not delivered by a real postman. A little girl, who went on using the title from force of habit, carried round the letters in place of her father, the real postman, who had lost the use of his legs from too much tramping to and fro and climbing up and down stairs. The arrangement had been made while a substitute was sought for, a solution desired by everyone but the sick man and his daughter Regina, who would be reduced almost to penury had they nothing but his retired pension to live on. But as things were, with the tips the child often got when she delivered a parcel, they could live decently enough.

There was usually a large post for the school. Andrés was the boy who got fewest letters. He was an orphan, and wrote only to his uncle and guardian, Alejo Vidal—'that old reprobate Vidal'. Andrés called him this in his thoughts because once, on a visit, a party of ladies thinking he was not listening had used this insulting expression about his guardian. He thought the description witty. He liked it. Such things amused little Andrés.

Having left the letters in the courtyard, Regina went out by the iron gate. Andrés, who had received no letter, went out with her. It was Thursday afternoon, when the boys had permission to go down to the beach.

'What have you got in that basket, Regina?'

'Some pomegranates.'

'I've never tasted pomegranates. Do give me one.'

'Indeed I won't! They're for my father. A lady gave them to me.'

'You'll eat one yourself on the way home, and not worry about your father going short, so why not give me one?'

'I shan't eat any,' protested the little girl, 'and even if I did, I'm my father's daughter and I've a perfect right to.'

'But you wouldn't be doing me a kindness, you'd be doing it for your own sake. If you give me one, you'll get back a hundred.'

'Oh yes, I dare say! A hundred!' the little girl said, laughing loudly as townspeople do. 'Do you mean to say that if I give you one pomegranate I shall be able to take my father a hundred?'

'Yes, that's right.' Andrés turned his head and looked at the little girl who went on laughing.

'Why are you looking at me like that?'

'I was trying to imagine what you would look like when you're a little old woman. Your eyes will still shine like two marbles, but almost all the rest will be gone.'

'Almost all the rest of what?'

'Your life.'

Regina looked serious. Andrés had said the word 'life' in a terrifying tone of voice.

'How old are you, Regina?'

'Going on for eleven.'

'Don't say "going on". It's a vulgar way to talk. Besides, who knows if you're going or not going. You might fall dead this very moment. I'm twelve.'

Regina gazed at Andrés. She remembered often seeing him look like this: serious, standing very stiff and straight with feet apart and hands in pockets. He looked just the same when he was first brought to the school as a very small boy, and went out into the garden to look at the pigeons. And then, as now, a lock of dark hair hung over his forehead. 'Push your hair back or you'll grow a squint,' she had said to him. She said it again this evening. The boy had grown quite a lot these last years. There was no reason now to go on calling him 'little Andrés'.

'Well anyhow, do let me just touch a pomegranate.'

Andrés took the fruit and stroked it carefully as if he were stroking the cheek of a sleeping baby. Then he put it back in the basket.

'Shall I tell you something, Regina? Yesterday I saw Livia Aivil.'

'Who's she? I don't know her. Does she live here?'

'No, she comes from somewhere else.'

'Where?'

'No special place. Another place.'

'But where does she live?'

'She doesn't live.'

'What *are* you talking about?'

Andrés brushed the lock of hair back from his forehead with a deliberate gesture. He raised his eyes over Regina's head to the horizon.

'She was alive once. She came in a boat which was wrecked on the shore.'

'But then how can you say you saw her?'

'She came this morning to look for her hair-ribbon.'

'You're just trying to scare me, Andrés!'

Andrés burst out laughing till the tears came into his eyes.

'Yes, that's it—I want to frighten you.'

Regina started to run off along the beach. Andrés's voice followed her:

'But all that about Livia Aivil is quite true!' he cried. 'It is, really. She came to look for the blue ribbon she used to tie her hair with. The wind had blown it away. Really, Regina! I promise you.'

Regina did not hear his last words. The only person who heard them was Livia Aivil, who approached at that very moment, jumping between the rocks and looking for her little blue hair-ribbon lost more than a hundred years ago.

Little Andrés was the sort of boy who would have believed that donkeys could fly if he had been told so. He would have believed it for the simplest possible reason: because he had seen donkeys fly.

III

REGINA ran along the beach with her basket of pomegranates on her arm.

Travellers who arrived for the first time at that east-coast town were amazed by its beauty, by the purity of the blue sky and the crystalline transparency of the air; by the radiance of the light which made all its colours glow. But Regina saw none of that. She had been born and bred there and took no stock of all the beauty which surrounded her. Yet beauty so brilliant, even when it goes unnoticed, strikes one with a sort of fear, sends obscure terrors creeping into the soul. It lies like an oppressive weight upon the heart.

At night in winter-time the waves used to pound upon the rocks and the wild sound of the sea echoed in every cranny. But Regina was not afraid of the sea. What she was afraid of without even knowing it was something quite different: the blazing light of summer afternoons, the translucent blue-green horizon, and the stars which spangled the night sky in spring.

While she ran, leaving her small footprints behind her in the wet sand, she felt stirred by disturbing sensations, both frightening and delicious. This secret anxiety, this emotion swelling within her breast as if to burst it, must be what Andrés so gravely spoke of as 'Life'.

When she got home she found her father in a bad temper as usual. Poor Dimas could not bear his infirmity patiently. Sitting in an armchair all day long, when not actually in bed, with nothing to do but read and curse his fate—it was no life at all for a man under fifty and used to getting about! Worse still if he had not had his reading. This had been Regina's idea. A great many newspapers passed through her hands; it was too bad that the poor invalid should not enjoy them. Bit by bit he became very skilful at opening the packets without leaving any trace. One day he tried a letter. In the end he opened them all. Regina used to steam open the envelopes. She felt some scruples about this, and consulted Andrés.

'Don't worry,' the boy told her. 'Special allowances have to be made for people who are ill. Haven't you seen them eat meat on fast days?'

'And don't you think reading the letters of a whole town is any worse than eating meat?'

'It comes to the same thing. It's only a question of

degree; and the Church disapproves of too many
scruples. You needn't worry about it.'

'But I do.'

'Well then, why don't you confess?'

'I'm afraid to. Supposing after all it turns out to be
a sin, what's to be done? I can't take such a pleasure
away from my father, especially now when such inter-
esting letters keep coming from the chemist!'

'Yes, that's quite true. It's dangerous to ask for
advice,' the boy argued. 'This is the sort of question
you ought to put direct to the Pope.'

In the end they reached a solution. They agreed that
the boy would take the responsibility for the offence,
if such it were. By means of a friendly arrangement
Andrés *bought* her sin from Regina.

'Father,' she said as she came in, 'Doña Asuncion
gave me these pomegranates for you. She says they'll
do you good because they're full of vitamins.'

'Vitamins!' complained the sick man. 'That's just
another fairy story made up by the ladies from the
Charity Committee, so as not to have to give us anything but tomatoes and rubbish. What would do me
good would be some nice slices of loin of pork, not
vitamins—they're no food for a man.'

'Don't be so silly, Father. You know the doctor said
you mustn't eat fat.'

'Much good the doctor is, either. They're all the same.'

He struck the open pomegranate which his daughter was offering him, and the small seeds, shining and appetizing, scattered on to the floor. The little girl picked them up without grumbling and put them in her mouth.

Dimas went on holding forth. When he once began grousing he always kept it up for quite a time.

'Why don't you talk the Valencian dialect any more, Father?' asked the child.

'Because I don't want to.'

Regina was silent. She remembered that when she was very small they used to speak the local dialect at home: but later on, after the death of her mother (who came from Palmar), the widower had little by little returned to the way of speech of his own people, for he was a Castilian from Orillares and had come to the east coast as a bachelor.

'At least,' his daughter said boldly, 'you do swear in Valencian.'

Her father did not hear, or if he did he decided not to answer such a stupid remark, and he went on to heap insults on Santa Rita, who for some extraordinary reason always had to bear the brunt of his dissatisfaction.

Regina had consulted Andrés about this too.

'Santa Rita was an Italian,' said the little boy, 'so she's sure to understand Spanish as the two languages are so much alike; but I expect your dialect is less well

known in heaven. Tell him to do his swearing in
Valencian.'

The little girl went into the kitchen to get supper
ready. Soon afterwards she went round to a neigh-
bour's house to ask for a clove of garlic.

'You're a perfect nuisance with your borrowing,
child,' grumbled the widow Sandrach, at whose door
the girl had knocked. 'You're always coming round
getting things from one house or another, and then
you forget to give them back.'

'I don't forget,' said Regina. 'I always remember.'

'Well, I like your cheek, I must say. Then why
don't you return them, my girl?'

'Because if I don't,' answered the child gravely, 'and
if you really give me the things, God will have to pay
you back a hundred for every one you give.'

She didn't hear the widow Sandrach's insulting
reply, because at that moment her father called her
angrily from the other house.

After supper she helped her father into bed and then
carried the candle into the kitchen. She set to work to
wash the dishes, and when she had finished put the
candle on a chair and crouched on the floor reading
Genoveva de Brabante.

IV

A WEEK after the beginning of term two new boys came to the school; they arrived late because they had been having mumps, as they very unwisely told their new companions.

Two fat little boys who start their school life by talking about mumps are doomed to be bullied from the word go.

They were brothers and their names were Rafael and Ricardo. The fact that the elder of the two called the younger Dickie only made matters worse. From the first they were 'the mumpish dickey-birds'. Add to this that they were not very bright, and it will be easily understood how a furious campaign of hitting and teasing the two unfortunate fat boys soon became the great feature of this term. If only they had been good at their lessons they could have joined the 'swots' under the leadership of Francisco; but, vague and simple-minded as they were, there was no hope for them. They were relegated to a sort of no-man's-land, a small island where they were constantly subject to attack from two separate armies.

22

On the day of their arrival, Javier made an abortive attempt to enrol them on his side. Javier was the leader of the rebels (nearly all of whom were behind-hand with their school work) and he had for the moment the idea of using Rafael and Ricardo as shock troops. But he soon gave this up when he found out that the 'dickey-birds' were cry-babies. He was ready to have almost anyone in his gang—did in fact have a very mixed lot—with the sole exception of cry-babies. The boys under his command might break a leg or arm, be covered with scars for the best part of the term, or have stones thrown at them, but their only reaction to physical pain must take the form of manly oaths—never tears.

After the first battle Ricardo's nose was bleeding and he was blubbing like a child. Of course he really was a child, hardly ten years old in fact, but that was no excuse. The rules of Javier's gang had some points in common with those of the Foreign Legion. 'Our members defy death' was the motto of their leader. Neither Rafael nor Ricardo was at all inclined to defy death.

Andrés found the two brothers in the school yard after the battle. Dickie was moaning as he mopped up the blood flowing from a swollen lip with his hand-kerchief.

'We'll pay them back for this!' shouted Rafael at the top of his voice.

'It doesn't look to me as if you would,' remarked little Andrés. 'On the contrary; they'll beat you again, and each time much harder. You've seen they can do it; it's very bad indeed when they get it into their heads to rag a boy.'

'Well, really! Is that the only advice you have to offer us?'

Andrés had already thought of some different advice to help the two boys in their misery; but it seemed to him too soon to speak of it yet. Better to wait until they were in a proper state to understand it.

At all events a little talk about heroism and patriotism might comfort them a bit. Just because one was studying for one's baccalaureate, which was a distinctly pacific occupation, no need to turn up one's nose at military glory. Fighting as they had fought that afternoon, two against seven, they might have been the defenders of Numancia, putting up a front against the French on the Second of May. In fact, with what strength they possessed, had they not contributed their little bit to maintain the glory of the Spanish infantry?

So thick did Andrés lay it on that, when an hour later a trumpet sounded and the flag flying on the school roof was lowered, each of the brothers, aflame with patriotism, had his eyes full of tears.

It was several months later. No one could have said

that during this time Rafael and Ricardo had behaved like heroes. No. When danger threatened they usually turned tail and ran like rabbits; which did not save them, however, from a great many kicks and blows. It was now that Andrés decided that the right moment had come to tell them what, in his considered opinion, should be the goal and purpose of their lives.

He found them in the garden, some way from all the other boys. Both brothers were contemplating with great concentration one of Dickie's fingers which was swollen up like a potato.

'He's been stung by a wasp,' volunteered Rafael.

'What you must do,' advised little Andrés, 'is bite it as hard as ever you can, until the sting comes out.'

Dickie did as he said, but the sting did not come out; and the bite only made the finger hurt more than before.

'Leave it alone. It's better as it is,' then said little Andrés. 'Tonight you'll roll about in bed with the pain like a mad cat, but tomorrow it'll all be over. You must just grin and bear it.'

'Bear it until tomorrow? I'd rather go to the hospital and get them to cut my finger off!'

'Perhaps that would be better. It would hurt even more, if anything, and you might even get blood-poisoning.'

The two brothers stared at Andrés in dismay. Up till now he had been the only one to stay neutral throughout their recent troubles. What could have made him change so suddenly?

And now he said: 'I've been thinking that, as things are, the best thing you can do is to make up your minds to follow the path of martyrdom.'

'What? What on earth are you talking about?'

He let his gaze travel over the two small figures standing in front of him, as if to take stock of their wounds: their legs covered with scabs and weals, their bruised and battered heads, the long scar across Rafael's forehead.

'Listen; you must dedicate yourselves to martyrdom. It's the only way to turn your troubles into happiness and your defeats into victories. Don't do anything to that finger for the present, Dickie. Leave the sting to come out on its own, and put up with it. If you put up with it well, that'll be a sign that you're beginning to be a good martyr.'

The two brothers made no reply. They didn't know if Andrés was making fun of them or not. Nor did he say another word himself. He turned on his heel and went off across the garden in the direction of the iron gate. After a few minutes the elder of the brothers said to the smaller:

'Come on, let's go to the Sanatorium.'

'No, I'm not going.'

'Why not?'

'Because I don't want to.'

'Doesn't it hurt any more?'

'Yes, it hurts more than ever.'

'Well then, what are you going to do?'

'Bear it, stupid!' answered the little boy heroically.

LITTLE Andrés followed the track which led to the wayside shrine. He had to climb a steep hill on the way to the Asylum—a stony, dusty hill, which had once been a road but at present was seldom used. To get to the shrine one had to take a path winding down to the left. At the bottom, looking out on the sea like a stranded ship, lay the white bulk of the Asylum.

Near the top of the hill Andrés came across Javier, sitting on a stone and looking preoccupied.

'What's up?' he asked him.

Though he did not belong to his gang, Andrés was a firm friend of the leader of the rebels, and also felt for him that natural admiration which every boy feels for the worst boy in the school, and very seldom for the best.

'Sabotage,' the boy answered laconically.

After a silence heavily charged with pessimism he went on: 'Garciarena and Márquez are in the San. with sore throats.'

This dramatically bleak news more than accounted for Javier's expression of gloom. A centre-forward and a half-back of his own team put out of action on the very eve of the match against the Fifth!—under so terrible a catastrophe only someone with nerves of steel, like Javier, could even keep up a semblance of calm.

'And you say it was sabotage?'

'Yes, of course.' As he described what had happened the boy grew heated, as people usually do who blame others for their misfortunes. 'On Monday morning, after the practice game, the members of the Fifth invited Garciarena and Márquez to drink iced lemonade. They'd never treated them to anything before—not even water. They did it in relays.'

It was obviously a plot. The extraordinary thing was the innocence, the stupidity, one might say, of Garciarena and Márquez, in falling into the trap.

'And won't they be all right by Sunday?' asked Andrés.

'Not a chance. The doctor says it'll be at least four days. I ask you!—drinking iced lemonade when you're drenched with sweat!'

'Then what are you going to do? Scratch?'

'No, that's what they want—then they can say we're afraid.'

'And it's quite true,' little Andrés said. 'You *are* afraid.'

He thought of that mountain of human flesh Manolo Ordóñez, the centre-forward of the Fifth, whose heavy feet left bare patches on the grass of the football ground.

'I think you're done for,' was Andrés's comment, and after a pause he added in soft and dulcet tones: 'Five—nil.'

'What did you say.'

'Nothing. I was thinking about the score-board on the day of the match.'

Javier looked at Andrés, but decided just in time that he was too small and weak to hit.

'I've just thought of something.'

'What's that?'

'Yes, really,' began Andrés, 'I think there may be a solution.'

'What? Come on, tell me quickly!' cried Javier impatiently, for he was tired of racking his brains to find one.

'I think I have two good players for you, to take the place of the casualties.'

'Who?'

'The "dickey-birds".'

In any other circumstances Javier would have burst out laughing, but this was too tragic a situation for joking.

'Are you mad? Those fat chaps?'

'Those fat chaps are as hard as steel when they want to be.'

'I dare say, but in fact they never do want to be. What fearful rot you do think up!'

'Honestly you ought to try them. I'll vouch for them.'

'Have you ever seen them play?'

'No, they don't know how. They never have. But still they can learn.'

Javier tried to give a sarcastic laugh, but it emerged as a sort of neigh.

'Learn? Between now and Sunday?'

'Horace learned to play the flute when he was eighty years old,' said little Andrés.

This fact had not the smallest bearing on the matter in hand, but a display of culture always has an effect, and on this occasion it impressed Javier for a few moments. After which he saw things in their true light again.

'Patricio, the Játiva Football Club forward, is very short and rather fat,' argued Andrés, in support of his suggestion.

'Good lord, yes, but Patricio plays like a lion!'

The honourable title of 'lion' was one of many which 'the dickey-birds' did not qualify for.

'You can be sure of one thing,' said Andrés finally, 'that Rafael and Ricardo will be a fearful hindrance to the enemy ranks, and that their team won't be able to move a step without running into a fat little boy.

Besides there are ninety-nine chances to one that they will fight like tigers.'

They had reached the wayside shrine. Javier stayed outside chasing lizards, while Andrés went in alone.

VI

AFTER he had deposited three pesetas in the poor-box—an offering which was closely connected with his success in the exams—Andrés went and knelt down in the chapel of Our Lady of Grace, Estrella de los Navigantes.

On either side of the image hung ex-votos placed there by the faithful recipients of some favour, granted through the mediation of the Virgin. There were crutches, feet and hands made out of wax, and one or two locks of hair. And away in one corner there were two plaits of chestnut-coloured hair, now somewhat moth-eaten, each tied at the end with a piece of shrivelled ribbon. Andrés looked at them for a long while. They were Regina's plaits. And he remembered yet again the time when she first made an offering of them.

It was at the beginning of Dimas's illness. His legs had begun to fail him and were getting worse every day; Regina had already taken over his postman's duties. She was in mourning for her mother at the time, and used to dress in neat black, with her two well-combed plaits falling over her shoulders to her waist. Her face had grown sad and thoughtful, and she no longer went skipping off to the gardens to feed the pigeons, laughing loudly.

It was Andrés who had the idea. Why not offer up her two lovely plaits to Our Lady of Grace, Estrella de los Navigantes, begging her to make her father well again?

The little girl agreed to the sacrifice, but lacked the necessary determination. She stood in front of the looking-glass with the scissors in her hand, but her courage failed her.

'I want to do it, you know,' she explained to Andrés, 'but it's just as though someone held my hand. It must be the devil.'

'I'll cut them off for you.'

And he did. So that the offering should be as splendid as possible, Andrés cut the plaits so near her head that the child was left almost bald.

'I look like a monk,' she said when she saw herself in the glass.

'No, Regina,' amended Andrés; 'it's Joan of Arc you look like.'

They went together to the wayside chapel to put up the ex-voto. Regina carried her plaits wrapped up in tissue-paper which she had begged from the confectioner's.

They knelt down and prayed fervently. Next to them a woman was praying also. They knew her. It was Orosia, from the ironmongery in the suburb of San Diego. They had heard that her daughter was dying.

'It's little Rosita,' whispered Regina. 'She has a chill on her chest.'

They went on praying for a long time, until the chapel was shut up for the night.

As all this passed through his mind, Andrés went on studying the ex-votos. There, next to Regina's plaits, was a small torso of wax which was already turning yellow. It was the chest of Rosita, the little girl from the suburb of San Diego.

For Rosita had made a marvellous recovery. Whereas poor Dimas got worse every day.

'The Virgin must have made a mistake,' said Regina, 'and performed our miracle for Rosita.'

It was some time before the whole truth came out. One day, when Andrés and Regina were talking, they confided to each other certain extra details.

'I did pray for the little girl a bit too,' confessed Andrés.

'So did I,' said Regina, 'I prayed for her a lot.'

'I told you the Estrella de los Navigantes couldn't make a mistake. You mustn't be sad. Our miracle wasn't taken away from us, we made a present of it ourselves.'

A ray of sunlight, creeping through the narrow window, happened to fall just upon Regina's plaits.

It seemed to Andrés as if exactly the opposite had happened: that it was the plaits which were shining, and sending out a beam of light which shot up through the window towards the sky.

VII

WHEN Andrés came out of the chapel he found Javier with his pockets full of lizards and stones.

It was a glorious evening; the sun was setting, and a few white clouds like great tufts of thistledown sailed across the blue sky towards the west.

If they got special permission the boys were allowed to be out of school till half-past nine, but most of them had gone off in several charabancs to visit the castle at Montesa, and would not be back until even later.

'Shall we go to the cemetery?' asked Javier.

'Yes. Come on.'

They often took this walk. Javier used to boast to his friends that he ate mulberries from a tree growing in the family tomb of the Guevaras and that they tasted of death, or horrify them with other macabre stories of his own invention. And little Andrés liked the secluded atmosphere of the graveyard, with its rows of dark cypresses and the rotten smell of the flowers which lay withering on the graves.

They climbed the hill, stooping now and again to pick up a stone and put it in their pockets. Like all boys they loved collecting curious stones.

The iron gate into the cemetery creaked as they opened it and its thick covering of ivy rustled. Such portentous sounds were quite disturbing enough to make Andrés's heart beat faster.

The most important monument in this humble village graveyard was the family tomb of the Guevara family, built at the beginning of the century in the form of a small temple with four columns, inside which a huge stone had been carved into the shape of an open book. On its pages, in bronze letters, were inscribed the names of the Guevaras with their dates of birth and death.

Andrés almost knew them by heart and felt that he had known them personally: Don Gabino Guevara y Guevara, 1801–1850; Doña Prudencia Guevara y Guevara, 1830–1860; Angelita Guevara y Monreal, 1845–1860. How did this Angelita Guevara y Monreal happen to die in the flower of her youth, at fifteen years of age? And why was there another Angelita Guevara, 1915–1930, further down nearly at the bottom of the list? Who was this second fifteen-year-old girl, who had followed in the footsteps of the first a century later? Had the first one never really died? The last burial, the last name engraved on the stone in letters that were still new and shining, was that of

Narciso Guevara y Nonell, 1881–1950. Javier and Andrés could remember seeing the old gentleman's funeral procession go by, followed by the whole town and by strangers as well.

There was still room on the pages of the stone book for more dead Guevaras.

Andrés stopped in front of the square white slab, enclosed within a low wall, on which in big black letters was the brief inscription: '*A i sui figli, la patria lontana,*' 1853.

Gazing at it, he saw that it was made of a different sort of marble from the rest. It was not a local stone. It must have been brought a very long way, from the great quarries of Carrara. It came across the sea to honour the memory of some Italians who were drowned on the east coast of Spain, a century ago. Running on to a reef, the ship had split in two and all on board had perished. All the bodies except one had been thrown up by the sea.

'The body of Livia Aivil was never recovered,' said Andrés to Javier after telling him this story. 'All the rest were identified and the only one missing was little Livia.'

'She must have been eaten by sharks,' said Javier.

'No, that wasn't what happened. Livia Aivil managed to save herself from the wreck, probably by holding on to the wing of her guardian angel. And you know angels can swim splendidly.'

'Don't talk nonsense! A boat must have picked her up. What happened to her afterwards?'

'I tell you she was never seen again. But she wasn't drowned. She's still alive.'

'What do you mean? Wasn't it a whole century ago that all this you've told me about happened? Of course it was; just look at the slab. Here it says: 1853!'

'That's nothing,' replied Andrés. 'Time has nothing to do with this sort of thing, you see. Livia Aivil is eternal. It's not a question of a hundred years ago, or two hundred, or even a thousand. She's always the same, until eternity. And she can't die, nor drown, nor anything, because she always exists in the present.'

Javier burst out laughing. 'You do think of silly things!'

They walked on in silence. Cleaning his hands with his handkerchief, for they were stained with mulberry juice, Javier read aloud the names inscribed on the tombstones. Nearly all of them were well cared for, clean, and bright with plants or flowers, showing that the prosperous little town piously honoured its dead. Only one of the graves seemed neglected, and looked quite a century old though it was nothing of the kind. The burial had in fact taken place less than three years ago. Yet it was hardly possible to read the letters: Brígida Pelín, 1885–1950.

'I knew her,' said Javier. 'Didn't you?'

'No; who was she?'

'Ah, of course! She died the winter before you came here to school. Do you know what we used to call her? The old hag.'

'Why?'

Javier told what he knew about the late Brígida Pelín. She had been in charge of the telegraph office for twenty years. She dressed in black; she was ugly and dirty and malignant-looking. Everyone complained of her bad temper, her rudeness and her disagreeable character. She was not a native of the town, nor did she come from anywhere in the neighbourhood, and none of her relations had ever been seen.

'Just think, when she died they found nothing in her house but a stinking old cat!'

'No!'

'Yes, a disgusting stuffed cat, so old and dirty that it was going rotten. That was her only companion while she lived here. When we went to send a telegram or telephone to someone, we always knew we were in for a blowing-up of some sort from the old hag. She was a horrid, cross old maid. We used to call her "the stinker" at school.'

Javier stopped talking and looked at the blackened stones of the tomb, as if he could see through them to the dead woman below.

'You can't imagine what she looked like,' he went on; 'greenish face and black teeth, thin greasy hair; hands like claws. She used to let the nails of her little fingers grow, and I tell you it made me feel quite sick to see them, all yellow and pointed. She was so stingy that she wouldn't turn on the electric light, and you could see her sitting by the window in the dark at night time, with her thin face as green as a witch's in the moonlight. They said she never lit a fire except once a week and ate all her food cold to save money.'

Andrés, much impressed, gazed for a long time at the dark, neglected tombstone, over which lizards were running, and his heart was fully of pity.

'Look, there's an eagle!' cried Javier.

They looked up at the sky. A solitary bird, which indeed looked like an eagle, was crossing the vast emptiness.

It was beginning to get dark. On the way home they took a short cut past the convent. When they reached the convent gate they saw a bundle lying at the foot of the steps. They went up to it.

'Look! It's a baby!'

Both boys had read of such things in books, but they had never believed they could really happen.

VIII

J AVIER, the more self-possessed of the two, picked up the little creature to have a better look at it. The little body, which was half naked, had been wrapped round in a piece of stiff stuff, which looked like part of an old sail. And from the baby's half-opened mouth there flowed a small trickle of milk from its last meal.

'What a cruel thing, to go and abandon a new-born baby like this!' exclaimed Javier, laying the bundle down on the steps again for fear of dropping it.

'It can't have any parents,' said Andrés.

'No parents? Why, it must have been its brute of a mother who left it here.'

'It can't have any parents,' repeated little Andrés. 'It must be a sylph. Sylphs never have parents.'

'There aren't any such things.'

'Of course there are. Here is one: small and round as a cheese.'

'Now you're off on your nonsense again.'

43

'It's asleep—and doesn't even know it's been born.'

'Babies don't open their eyes for eight days, like kittens,' said Javier knowingly.

Andrés, squatting down, gently touched the tiny smooth hand with one finger, and the baby opened its eyes.

'It's looking at us.'

'It can't see us. I tell you babies and kittens . . .'

'Oh, do shut up about babies and kittens!' interrupted Andrés. 'A sylph is a sort of airy spirit, who comes down from the sky like a good angel, to comfort human beings. I read about it in a dictionary.'

'Do you mean to say you believe this baby came here out of the sky?'

'Why not? You saw for yourself that nobody put it on the steps. And obviously no one knows how or when it got here. Why couldn't it have dropped out of the sky? I can't think why you say its mother brought it here. Have you seen a mother anywhere about? But don't you remember the eagle?'

'Are you going to tell me the eagle carried it here in its beak? Look here, Andrés, that's just make-believe, not what really happens.'

'It does happen, Javier, I tell you. It happens every day and every minute; but we don't notice.'

'Well, I do notice that you're always mooning away up in the clouds.'

'If you only knew the extraordinary things that go on up in the clouds!' said the boy seriously.

'Oh, very well! But all the same I think we ought to do something about it,' said Javier after a short silence. 'Tell the nuns; hand the baby over to them.'

'Wait a bit; not just this moment. First we must . . . have you got a calendar on you?'

'Yes, what d'you want it for?'

Andrés looked very solemn, and answered in a slow serious voice, as if coming to an important decision:

'We're going to christen the baby.'

'Us?'

'Yes. In an emergency anyone who has taken his First Communion can do it.'

'Don't be such an idiot! It must be christened properly! The baby isn't dying anyway.'

'We don't know if the baby's dying or not.'

Javier was not convinced in the very least; but he thought a baptism might be quite an amusing way to wind up the afternoon's entertainment, as there was nothing much else to do.

Andrés brought water in the lid of a box of tintacks which he had in his pocket, and began preparing for the ceremony.

'Pick her up in your arms,' he told his friend.

'Are *you* going to baptize her? Oh no, really! I'm the

oldest. If anyone's going to baptize her it must be me.'

Andrés gave in on this point. But Javier had to promise to perform the ceremony very seriously and say all the proper words.

'I see you don't think I know how to baptize a baby,' he protested.

All the same they agreed to have a rehearsal first; then, after the calendar had been consulted, the ceremony itself began.

It was almost dark. In this remote corner, far away from the town, nothing was to be heard but the distant and solemn sound of the sea.

'In the name of the Father, and of the Son, and of the Holy Ghost, I baptize you Carlota, Emilia, Silvana, Presbítera,' said Javier in a voice of strange emotion.

Andrés added one word:

'Pelín,' he said.

'What?'

'The surname.'

'You never mention the surname at a christening!'

'In this one we do. It's the most important thing of all. When we hand her over to the nuns we must be able to say that we've christened her with a surname and everything.'

'And why Pelín, why Pelín of all things, the horrid, stupid name of that beastly old woman?'

'Just for that very reason.'

'But . . .'

'Shut up, someone's coming!'

For they had rung the door-bell and now they could hear the latch being unfastened.

IX

HALF an hour later, as they left the convent, after handing over their unusual bundle and giving an account of the christening, Javier asked again:

'Why Pelín?'

Then Andrés divulged his secret reasons:

'When I saw the poor old woman's tombstone I thought I must do something for her.'

'What a time to choose! Three years after the funeral!'

'One can always do something. You know one can.'

'What can one do?'

Andrés did not answer except by asking another question:

'Do you really mean that she had no one belonging to her, not even a sister-in-law?'

'The old hag? No one. When she died they had to distribute her few odds and ends among the poor, because she didn't seem to have any relations. And even the poor didn't want her rubbish! So they took the stuff to the Asylum, rather than throw it in the sea.'

Andrés brooded for a moment over the miserable chattels of old Brígida Pelín; he pictured the rubbish-cart going down to the Asylum with her wretched belongings, and his heart was frozen with sadness.

'The whole town hated her,' went on Javier. 'Even the dogs used to bark when they saw her, she was so ugly and dirty.'

'Well, that's all over now,' said little Andrés calmly. 'It's as if she had had a little daughter, a pale, plump, little baby girl. Carlota, Emilia, Silvana, Presbítera, Pelín.'

'Poor little thing! You *have* given her a fine mother!'

'She had nobody either. She was quite alone. But now at least she has a tomb where her name and her children's and grandchildren's names can be inscribed, like the Guevaras. She'll keep the headstone clean and put flowers all round, and look after it and keep it tidy as it should be. Don't you think she looked a clean little thing?'

And this was how it happened that the 'old hag', the much-hated Brígida Pelín, came to produce a flourishing family three years after her death. It was as if there had sprouted from her desolate grave, in the black night where birds of prey and hobgoblins were flying, a tender bud of light and life.

'Nothing ever dies, nothing is ever quite finished,'

D

thought little Andrés. 'The years follow each other, one by one, until at last they build up centuries and centuries.'

When they got near the school the boys separated. They would have to invent excuses for being late. Javier began to run. He didn't want to get kept in, with the match just coming on. Andrés walked slowly back alone.

Night had fallen. A sharp gust of wind struck him in the face. He couldn't see where it came from.

'It must be the eagle just flying away,' he said to himself, 'the eagle which brought the tiny body of Carlota Pelín, the sylph.'

X

THE 'dickey-birds' went to look for Andrés, so as to report on their progress in the hard path of martyrdom. His verdict was that their success had been so remarkable that they were now within sight of the goal. But, of course, it must be borne in mind that the present day was different from the times of the Emperor Diocletian, who by his cruel persecution of the Christians had made things much easier for would-be martyrs. In the modern world religious toleration and the disappearance of the Roman arena put obstacles in the way of realizing a quick and effective plan to become a martyr; however, as things were, they could hardly have done better.

Rafael, the elder of the two brothers, exhibited a swollen knee, enveloped in bandages.

'Water on the knee,' he announced with a suggestion of pride.

'A kick,' supplemented the younger brother.

'What a pity,' said Andrés. 'Jolly bad luck! You won't be able to run very well in the match.'

'What match?'

'On Sunday.'

'But *I'm* not playing!' protested the boy.

Andrés looked hard at the two brothers. If he had been looking for two boys as far as possible removed from the physical type required for an athletic team of any sort or kind, selected even on the most lenient principles, the 'dickey-birds' would have filled the bill: fat, short, clumsy, and nearly always out of breath, they were the sort of boys who got given a puzzle or a set of dominoes for Christmas, but never a tennis-racket or a riding-whip.

'I had thought you might play instead of Márques and Garciarena.'

Human vanity is ever susceptible to flattery, and the two little would-be martyrs were no exception. The fact that somebody thought them capable of taking the place of two of the best players for the Fourth in a match so important as next Sunday's, could hardly fail to thrill them. But their skill at games fell so fantastically short of what was required that they could not help protesting:

'What *are* you talking about? If Javier heard you he'd think you'd gone crazy!'

'Javier did hear me and he did think I'd gone crazy; but in the end I convinced him.'

'Convinced him of what?'

The 'dickey-birds' were so astounded that they could not make head or tail of it.

'I took the liberty of answering for you,' said Andrés, 'and I promised him you would play like lions.'

'Oh no! No!' protested both brothers at once, abandoning in their agitation the thorny path of martyrdom.

'Do you want to miss the torments of the arena?'

After a few moments' consideration the 'dickey-birds' quickly decided that the scenes in the Roman arena must have been a mere joke compared to the probable horrors of the football-field next Sunday. They were quite sure, so they told little Andrés, that even in the Coliseum there had never been anything like it.

'Well, it's a great pity; now everyone will say you've backed out—that you've funked it.'

'Backed out be blowed! We never said we'd play!'

'I said it for you, though. I even thought of a good nickname for you, what they call a *nom de guerre.*'

'What was it?'

'It's hardly worth while telling you, since you're not going to use it.'

'Tell us, anyway—what was the name?'

'The Jackals of Mondoñedo.'

Very few little boys could have resisted the subtle

magic of such a nickname. The 'dickey-birds', whose family did in fact come from the cathedral town of Mondoñedo, could not help seeing how suitable was the title hit upon by Andrés, and as a result, each of them began to feel his firm decision not to play begin to totter on its foundations. Little Andrés understood this and thought it advisable to return quietly to the charge.

'The hermits who lived in the desert,' he began, 'used to mortify the flesh by fasting and sack-cloth and ashes, and whipping and so on. In fact, the sort of thing which isn't allowed by the school rules. There'll be just as many difficulties in our way if we try and find another sort of martyrdom.'

He paused for a moment to see if the 'dickey-birds' were listening, and seeing that they were very quiet and attentive, he went on:

'Job purified his soul by sleeping in filth; but if you try that on you'll only be expelled from the school as disgusting pigs, and that won't get you any further. I don't say that later on you mightn't be able to get to the desert,' he said kindly, 'but there are some things you have to work up to bit by bit.'

'Are there any deserts still?' asked one of the boys, aware of the feebleness of his geographical knowledge.

'Of course there is one! Haven't you seen it at the cinema?'

Yes, they had seen *Beau Geste*. That cheered them up a bit.

'But for the moment you must be getting into training. You can't achieve perfection by a single kick or blow. You have to have lots of kicks and lots of blows one after another. You have to test your soul, to see if it's made of the right metal.'

The 'dickey-birds' felt that the kicks and blows that had so far come their way had not been administered to their souls at all; on the contrary, most of them had landed on that part of the anatomy which seemed to them furthest from the soul.

'Don't be so stupid! Your soul is what's inside your body. If you knock over a jug and break it, water runs out, doesn't it? Very well, the soul is like the water and the body is the jug. You have to let yourself be beaten so that your soul can come gushing out and refresh your rotten body.'

'Why rotten?' protested the boys.

'It's what the body is always called. I don't know why, but it always is, and that's good enough.'

Andrés was warming to his work as he talked. He saw the two 'dickey-birds' standing in front of him like two fat, clumsy jugs, and had no difficulty in believing that inside each of them there was a shining, heavenly spring. Inside everyone's body, even the bodies of stupid, lazy little boys, God had put a fountain of everlasting life, a trickle of pure and transparent water from the Jordan.

The result of this conversation was that the 'Jackals of Mondoñedo' agreed that they would at least take part in tomorrow's practice game, to show what they could do.

XI

ON Sunday morning the fever of excitement in the school had reached such a pitch that it seemed that if any two boys were to bump into each other sparks must fly. When they met any members of the teams who were to compete in the afternoon's match, they stood back and let them pass respectfully, as if, instead of their school-fellows, they had been the sacred cows of legendary India.

There was a tremendous clatter and chattering in the courtyards, and the boys rushed up and down stairs a thousand times to make sure that they had turned off the taps in the wash-basins, because in their excitable state they knew they were capable of any disastrous act of absent-mindedness.

The two disqualified athletes, Garciarena and Márques, received visits at regular intervals in the San. from the emissaries they had sent out to report on what was happening and on the state of the morale of their side.

As if all this were not enough, the collection for the

Church Mission was due to take place that very morning, and with the exception of the teams (who must save their energies) all the boys in the school had to go round the streets and houses with their collecting boxes and badges. For although it was not a monastery school the Headmaster had offered the help of his boys in aid of the Mission.

Francisco, with another boy, was chosen to visit the grandest houses in the town, because he was the most serious-minded boy in the school, as well as the best-dressed and the most articulate.

Francisco received this news with enormous satisfaction. He enjoyed the idea of giving himself airs, mixing with the cream of local society, and at the end of the day producing the largest sum of money.

'We shall visit the homes of the aristocracy,' he said to his companion Mariano, a sickly boy with a face like a fly.

Francisco always talked like this, not in fun but out of a sort of inborn pretentiousness, which Javier (who was maddened by it) called his 'congenital idiocy'.

'We shall collect a vast sum to help the Mission carry on their noble work of driving barbarism and idolatry out of Asia; and at the same time we'll do better than all the others, who won't collect more than about fourpence.'

'You think so?'

'I'm sure of it! The Marquesa will give us a most substantial donation. *Noblesse oblige.*'

'What?' asked his seedy companion, who had not understood the French words.

'Noble birth imposes obligations,' and to make matters clearer he added: 'It's a famous saying of La Rochefoucauld's.' For Francisco believed, not without a certain amount of reason, that all famous sayings had originated with La Rochefoucauld.

With which remark, he rang the bell hanging beside a door of polished wood framed in stone. This house belonged to the richest family in the town, that of Borrell the chocolate manufacturer, who paid the highest taxes in the district.

'We will begin with wealthy industry, go on to the upper middle classes, and end with the aristocracy.'

'Wealthy industry' sent them packing in no uncertain manner. There had been a mistake in making out the collectors' itineraries, perhaps due to the fact that the Borrells' great house stood at the meeting-point of three streets, with the result that it had been included in several lists; and Francisco and his companion happened to be the fourth party who had rung that bell in the hopes of saving Asia from idolatry. As the master and mistress of the house were away, and as the porter (who was old and rheumatic) had to make a fearful effort each time to get up from his chair and go down the seven steps to open the door, and as, moreover, he was quite without interest in the spiritual future of Asia—when he saw before him two more young persons armed with collecting-boxes and elaborate evangelical arguments, he threw them out with a violence so unexpected from one of his advanced age that it was a wonder the virtuous apostles of charity did not break their necks there and then.

Mariano suggested they give up the whole thing; but Francisco would not for worlds have gone back to school empty-handed.

'The upper middle classes keep porters too,' his feeble companion argued with great good sense.

Francisco paid no attention and went on following his prescribed route.

Meanwhile, as they set off towards the upper middle classes—who not only kept porters but watch-dogs too—back at the school the last collecting-boxes were being given out.

Javier, as captain of one of the teams, was supposed to take no part. But he was in such a strung-up state, and the time until five o'clock seemed to be dragging by so slowly, that he asked if he could join in the collecting.

Only one part of the town remained to be covered by the collectors, and this was always known to be the toughest proposition of the lot. This was a group of houses round the little harbour, whose inmates led a life apart. There was a café here, often the scene of drunken brawls, and seldom visited by the more peaceful residents of the rest of the town. But in spite of the squalor of its one street, the degraded-looking inhabitants of this quarter—the Island as it was called —were rumoured to have plenty of money; and it was suspected, not without foundation, that their wealth came from smuggling and crooked dealings rather than from honest work. Sinners and atheists all, they none of them ever went near the church. But recently their growing prosperity was shown by the installation of a magnificent football-machine in the Equality Bar.

The Headmaster of the school thought it would be asking for trouble to send two children to this neighbourhood, in hopes of collecting money for good works from such people. He explained to the boys that they might have stones thrown at them—it had happened before—and even if they were left in peace it would be most unlikely that they would get the smallest contribution. So that no detachment had yet been sent to the Island when Javier asked for a collecting-box and for permission to go to this rough quarter. Javier was tall for his age, broad-shouldered and tough-looking, so there seemed no great risk in his facing possible hostility.

'The worst that can happen is that we shan't get sixpence,' said the boy to the companion who was to go with him.

'We'll get more than anyone. More even than Francisco,' said the above-mentioned companion—who happened to be little Andrés.

And both set off towards the dreaded Island—so-called because it was in fact almost an islet, projecting into the sea and only joined to the shore by a narrow strip of land.

'Well, Jonah lived for quite a time in the stomach of a whale,' said little Andrés.

'That's got nothing to do with us!'

'Yes, it has, and it ought to encourage us. If a long time ago a chap could do such an extraordinary thing and come out alive, there's no reason why we shouldn't come out alive too. Just look at the Island, it's quite like a whale. But before we get there, let's take off our badges.'

'What for? It's against the rules.'

'What would be against the rules would be to go and annoy the enemy and get ourselves beaten up. There's no point in taking two innocent children and serving them up on a salver to those cannibals. It's our duty to defend Christian boys whenever we have a chance to do so—even when it so happens that those Christian boys are ourselves.'

So they took off their badges and entered the stomach of the whale.

XII

THE first thing that struck them when they arrived at the terrible Island was that the inhabitants seemed to spend Sunday morning asleep.

There was hardly anyone in the street, and in several houses the blinds were still down. A few bare-footed children—the offspring of those who were not expected to help convert the heathens in the Far East— were running along in the gutter. They stopped their game for a moment to stare inquisitively at Javier and his companion, laughed to see how absurdly respectable boys behaved, and then went on with what they were doing.

Further on, in the square, some groups of ill-favoured men were to be seen standing about or going in and out of the Bar, like characters in a French film.

Supposing that an imaginary painter received an urgent commission to paint a picture of the Last Supper, and supposing that in this quandary the only models available were those collected in the square of the Island this Sunday, he must have faced certain failure. Not a single virtuous or gentle face could the miserable man have found, much less twelve. He would even have had to search elsewhere for his Judas, for Judas's villainy was concealed by his beard, and here were none but shaven or half-shaven villains.

'Do you think they will lynch us?' asked Javier with laudable sang-froid.

'I don't think so,' replied Andrés. 'Places where they lynch you are more civilized than this wretched town.'

They were approaching the café, and could see through the window men playing cards and pushing large stakes across the table.

'I heard there was plenty of money here,' remarked Javier. 'The worst of it is we shall never get hold of it. Do you think they look as if they would be upset because there are babies in India or China who haven't been baptized? What do they care about the heathens!'

Andrés, for his part, was far from pessimistic.

'We needn't mention the heathens. These men are uneducated and don't understand that sort of thing. We shall have to approach them on their own level.'

'They aren't religious, though,' insisted Javier in a defeatist tone.

'Even irreligious people put their hands in their pockets when they want to.'

'Yes, of course, but they won't want to fork out their cash for the Pope.'

'I don't see the smallest necessity to mention the Pope. In fact, from what I've seen so far, I think this is one of the moments when to speak of the Holy Father might be most inappropriate.'

'What then?'

'We must go in for a certain amount of strategy. First of all, I don't think this Bar is a good place to start our campaign. It would be rash to go and seek out the enemy in the middle of all his vice and wickedness. Besides, if it came to a battle, I think we should do better in an open field.'

Javier approved of these prudent tactics, and together they walked towards the fountain in the square, where several people, mostly women, were gathering to fill their pitchers.

'Perhaps we could try asking for some water, to see if there's a Good Samaritan among them?'

But no, this was not at all a fashion which prevailed among the people of the Island. With varying degrees of rudeness they told the two boys that if they were thirsty they could drink from the spout. Neither of the boys was in the least thirsty, but they thought drinking from the spout might be democratic and make a good impression, so they did.

'When's the famous strategy going to begin?' asked

E

Javier impatiently, seeing that his friend was still looking passive and expectant.

'Now. But you must let me do the talking . . .'

They had chosen for their first approach to the enemy a group of old men who were basking in the sun on a stone seat. They were fairly decently dressed, and in spite of the look of depravity common to all the people of the quarter, a faint suggestion of nobility was lent to their faces by the white hair showing under their berets.

'Gentlemen,' said little Andrés, holding out his collecting-box to the group of old men, 'would you care to give a little contribution for the Foreign Atheists?'

Javier stared at Andrés open-mouthed.

'What do you say, boy?' asked one of the old men, either because he couldn't hear very well or because he couldn't understand the request.

Andrés made it more explicit:

'Please, gentlemen, help the poor Anarchists!'

The plan was soon proved to be an excellent one. In a short time both collecting-boxes were full of coppers, and even included one or two notes.

Cheered by their success, they went off to the Equality Bar. They must defeat the enemy in his own headquarters!

In the Bar their triumph was conclusive. They were called to table after table to take money.

They went out into the square beside themselves with delight.

As they started on their way home a huge grey dog came to meet them.

'Gris! Gris!' Andrés called to him, as if he was an old friend.

The creature ran up and licked his hand.

'Do you know him?' asked Javier in surprise.

'Yes. I've known him quite a long time.'

'But have you been to the Island before?'

'No, never. This is the first time. But that has nothing to do with it. Gris doesn't belong here, nor anywhere else, nor to any special time. He was alive a hundred years ago.'

'What?'

'Yes—let me think. He was living exactly a hundred and one years ago. In 1852.'

'Don't talk rubbish.'

They went on their way. Before they had left the isthmus which separated the Island from the rest of the town, Gris left them.

'Listen,' said Javier when they were nearly at the school, 'it seems to me we were wrong to deceive all those people. We got their money by lying.'

'Nothing of the sort!' protested Andrés quite angrily. 'On the contrary. We spoke to them clearly in a language they could understand. If we'd asked them for money for the Pope, as you wanted us to, then we should have been deceiving them. Neither the Pope nor all the Cardinals in Rome could have got a single crumb of bread out of the people of the Island. The money they gave us will help stop people being atheists and heathens and not believing in God—will go to people just like themselves in fact, only they live in Asia or India or China. And I said that about the "Poor Anarchists" so that they should understand exactly what they were meant to, and there should be no deception at all.'

XIII

THEY arrived at the school gate at the same time as Francisco and his companion. The young highbrow was pleased by this coincidence. It would gratify his vanity to humiliate his enemy.

It was tacitly accepted that there were two rival factions in the school, one led by Francisco and one by Javier. Ever since far-off days in the bottom form until now, when Francisco had swotted his way well ahead, the antagonism between the two hostile parties had steadily increased. They were like the Guelphs and the Ghibellines, or the Capulets and the Montagues, as Francisco elegantly explained.

'How did you get on with the riff-raff?' asked Francisco sarcastically. Although his own expedition had begun so badly, he had in the end succeeded in getting a hundred-peseta note out of the Marquesa—on whose munificence he had done well to rely, for she was very generous, rich and (better still) his grandmother.

Javier was just going to reply when Andrés interposed, foreseeing that words would soon lead to blows, as so often happens.

'It is easier for a camel to pass through the eye of a needle than a rich man through the gates of Paradise,' said little Andrés sententiously.

He knew that the ironical significance of this remark would satisfy Javier's desire for revenge, and on the other hand that its religious flavour would make them safe from further attack. With tense expressions, looking like two fighting-cocks with their hackles up, the two champions of Christian charity and their squires then made their way to the Headmaster's study for the examination of the collecting-boxes.

For a long time afterwards a story went about the school that the events of this day gave Francisco gall-stones as big as potatoes, which could even be seen through his clothes. No doubt this version erred on the side of exaggeration, yet taken purely symbolically it might be said to be true. With eyes starting from his head and face as white as a sheet, he stared at the 'river of gold'—as it seemed to him in his envy and bitterness—that gushed from Javier's collecting-box. Perhaps it was at this moment that there began to revolve in the mind of the studious Francisco certain ideas definitely hostile to the aristocracy.

Javier, with his large widely-spaced teeth showing

in a broad grin of triumph, indulged in the ecstasy of victory for a few moments. But it was fleeting. Almost at once he lost his triumphant expression and sank once more into deep gloom. The outlook for this afternoon's match was so bad! They had such a poor chance of beating the Fifth! Black despair overwhelmed him. He cursed himself over and over again for his inexcusable weakness in agreeing to take on the 'dickey-birds'. It sent cold shivers down his spine to remember the disastrous performance of the new players in the practice game, where they had revolved round the field like a couple of sacks, and had not once succeeded even in grazing the ball with their boots. Somehow the sight of the 'dickey-birds' stuffed into their sports rig had been in itself particularly disheartening. Their shorts were so tight that they looked like two balloons ready to fly off into space at the least breath of favourable wind.

Javier confided his fears to little Andrés.

'Don't worry,' he replied soothingly. 'I'll go and see them. I think the chief thing is to improve their morale a bit. You leave that to me.'

Immured in their bedroom, each sitting on his bed with his eyes glued to the ground, the 'dickey-birds' did not raise their heads when the door opened and Andrés came in. They were in the grip of emotions so overwhelming as to absorb all power of thought and produce a sort of unawareness of their surroundings.

They had just reached that stage of fear when even the sense of hearing vanishes.

'How are you feeling?' enquired little Andrés in a cheerful tone.

His voice was that of an optimistic doctor in a hospital for incurables.

An icy silence was the only reply.

'It's a splendid day!' went on Andrés, as if he had not noticed the dismal expressions of his two companions. 'We've been lucky in our weather!'

Four half-dead eyes fastened themselves on his face accusingly. With this heart-rending glance they seemed to say that they had spent the whole night in desperate prayers that it might rain, that it might snow, that tornadoes and tempests, hurricanes and earthquakes, might be unloosed upon them—if only the match could be prevented from taking place. So that, very naturally, such a banal remark in praise of the weather only sounded in their ears like the cruellest sarcasm.

With each moment that passed the silence grew denser and heavier, like those agonizing silences that occur before acrobats perform a double somersault.

It seemed to Andrés that his task of improving the 'dickey-birds'' morale was going to be much more arduous than he had thought at first. He realized that he must have recourse to desperate measures.

'You surely aren't *sorry* you're playing this afternoon?' he said, as if this was the most unlikely thing in the world.

In reply to this remark the 'dickey-birds' believed that they laughed, and in fact they opened their mouths to do so; but instead of the sarcastic and scornful laugh they had aspired to, there emerged only a sort of sneeze, such as a seal gives when his trainer flicks him with the whip.

In through the open window came the sound of childish voices, a cheerful holiday clamour. What a contrast with the despair which reigned in the 'dickey-birds'' bedroom!

'You mustn't be depressed,' Andrés told them. 'Anyone would think you were going to play against a team of cannibals!'

This was exactly the point of view held by the two brothers.

'Those beasts will kick us to pieces,' said Rafael.

'Oh, so that's what you're worrying about,' exclaimed little Andrés in a more cheerful tone. 'But that's the very thing you needn't fear at all. In a championship match there'll be a referee, you know, whose job it is to see that the play doesn't get too fierce. And apart from the referee, what do you suppose your guardian angels are for?'

'What? You don't suppose guardian angels play football, do you?'

'A jolly sight better than many internationals!'

This news seemed to put heart into Rafael but not into Ricardo.

'My angel is sure to be like me,' he said; 'he'll be fat, and bad at running, just like me.'

'Why should he run when he can fly?'

A gentle breath of wind seemed to blow through the room. In fact it was exactly as if a supernatural wing had fanned the air and left it lighter.

After a moment Andrés gave a great sigh, and said:

'I'm sorry to see that you've abandoned the path of martyrdom in such a cowardly way.'

'That's not true,' said Rafael firmly.

The little boy had his own views on the subject. To let oneself be slowly flayed alive by unknowns might be called an agreeable form of martyrdom; but to be pounded to pieces by the members of the Fifth before the whole school was really outside the limit.

'What limit?' said Andrés.

'The limit between sanity and madness.'

'There's no such limit,' said Andrés firmly.

'Why not?'

'In the sense you mean there's no difference at all between an idiot and a saint. The martyrs in Africa voluntarily let themselves be tortured by negroes and pygmies, and inferior races much lower and more revolting than the members of the Fifth.'

The 'dickey-birds' began to revive a little. Think-

ing of their adversaries as inferior races seemed somehow to change things. It was not that they had ceased
to feel afraid. But suddenly their fear had become
heroic.

XIV

TWENTY minutes before the match began every available place to watch it from was occupied. Not only all the benches set out for the purpose, but every wall or tree from which any glimpse of the field could be had. The relatives of the boys, sitting in the best seats, chatted together with an air of unconcern, as if this was just an innocent children's game which there was no need to take seriously; but at heart each of them was desperately keen that their side should win.

From the very beginning of the match the overwhelming superiority of the Fifth was plain. They took possession of the ball, as though the other eleven players had nothing to do with the matter. Javier, panting and sweating and half-undressed, did his level best, but he got little support from his side. He wanted to be in every threatened part of the field at once, but he kept finding his path barred by a small fat boy, staggering like one who has received a heavy blow.

The referee was Mr. Tild, the gym instructor, a Dane as tall as a church tower. The team of the Fourth thought that he had sold himself to the Fifth, and the Fifth thought he had been bought by the Fourth. The 'dickey-birds' for their part soon decided that the whole school had paid him to crack down on them alone. All these views were unjust. The admirable Mr. Tild was a fair-minded sportsman, who was prepared to be torn in pieces—and goodness knows he was often within an ace of it—rather than make an incorrect decision. But it was not always easy to be sure if there had been a foul, in the middle of play which was often far from clean.

Garciarena and Márques from the San. made up a fifth column hostile to the 'dickey-birds'. Both had done their best to get the match postponed until they were well enough to play, and in their disappointment they had collected a band of supporters to demonstrate against the new players.

Andrés realized that the situation was becoming critical. Everyone, from Javier who looked at him with accusing and furious eyes every time he collided with the impeding bulk of a 'dickey-bird', to the last spectator, agreed with one voice that it had been madness to thrust those fat boys into such a game. And—as Andrés nobly admitted—that madness had been his. 'Get rid of the fat boys!' was the most harmless of the comments shouted by the onlookers. No, it really was not possible to say that the 'Jackals of Mondoñedo' were the heroes of the day.

When the first half ended the score was one–nil in favour of the Fifth. But suddenly something happened which gave Andrés moral support. He saw a friend's face in the crowd.

Perched on top of a wall which separated the football ground from the cow-sheds, was Regina. The little girl was calmly preparing to watch the match while she ate a kilo of damaged peaches which had been given to her that morning, and which her father had rejected.

'You must "root" for us!' said Andrés, coming up to her.

Regina was ignorant of sporting terms and made him explain.

'Rooting for a side is making out they are in the right when they're not.'

'Oh, I see! And which is my side?'

'The Fourth, of course.'

'Good. I'll support them. How do I do it?'

'Egg them on; cheer them up; give them confidence in themselves.'

Regina could not imagine how to give the Fourth confidence in themselves; but she promised wholeheartedly to do the best she could, and as soon as the match started again she began throwing her peach-stones at the Fifth's players.

'Somebody is throwing things at our side,' complained Francisco from his privileged seat.

'Pooh, they're not so soft that they'll be upset by a girl throwing those little stones at them!' put in Andrés, who had discreetly stationed himself beside Francisco so as to thwart the enemy.

There were no more complaints. Boys of school age feel such a profound disdain for that contemptible and idiotic section of humanity known as 'girls' that from then on they took no more notice of Regina's sabotage.

The little girl, with excellent insight, saw that if anyone needed her moral support it was the 'dickey-birds', and it was to them that she now gave all her attention. Every time they came near her, she cried out: 'Rah! Rah!', an expression she did not understand, but which she guessed would be appropriate, as she had heard it at the cinema, in films about sport. It certainly inflamed the enthusiasm of the fat boys, who were now playing with incredible energy. Nothing could have been more astonishing than the courage with which the 'Jackals of Mondoñedo' now hurled themselves into the attack—and this time it was the other side they were attacking; they met the enemy face to face without shrinking, not even when in the course of the game other players more than once trampled them under foot.

The scoreboard with its 1–0 reminded little Andrés of his prophetic vision.

'It's like Jacob's dream,' he thought.

But Jacob's dream was to be appreciably modified.

XV

WHEN seven minutes of the second half had gone by, the most amazing things began to happen.

Javier was awarded a penalty, and scored from the free kick. For a few tense moments the score remained at one all. Then came the miracle.

One of the 'dickey-birds'—no one knew which—ran towards Manolo Ordóñez to tackle him. It was like something in the Bible. It might have been the meeting between David and Goliath, if David had been fat. A thrill went through the spectators. Whatever may be said about the lack of sensibility of our modern world, that lack of sensibility could not go to the lengths of witnessing with indifference the sacrifice of an innocent child. Manolo Ordóñez was like a mountain, like Etna or Vesuvius—one of those terrible mountains that harbour fire within. Andrés shut his eyes. Heartfelt prayers surged to his lips, one jumbled with the next, in a despairing flood. Suddenly a loud murmur ran through the crowd. Violently propelled by the head of one of the 'dickey-birds'—no one knew which—the ball had passed between the goal-posts. The 'Jackals', sweating and dripping blood, roared aloud like actual wild beasts. Having discovered that their feet served no purpose whatever, they were now making good use of two heads as hard as rocks, with which they could project the ball into space as if from a cannon.

The match ended in a victory for the Fourth, by two goals to one.

It must be admitted that the 'dickey-birds' ' parents had come most unwillingly to the match. They were deeply displeased that the best mark either of their sons had gained throughout the term was a gamma. Their mother, who was inclined to be tolerant of her sons' idleness so long as their health was good, had persistently repeated that Latin proverb *mens sana in corpore sano* (a proverb which has so greatly increased the illiteracy on the shores of the Mediterranean). But even she had at last come to see that all was well with *corpore* and that the time had come to take *mens* seriously. As a result, father and mother had agreed together to tell the boys that if they did not make the grade in their school work they would be punished that summer by having no seaside holiday.

By the end of the match, however, this drastic decision had been considerably modified.

'We'll buy you a football this summer,' said their father.

'For you to practise with on the beach,' went on their mother.

But the 'dickey-birds' refused with conscious rectitude.

'We shan't be going to the seaside,' said the younger.

'What?'

'No,' said the elder of the two 'Jackals of Mondoñedo'; 'this year we thought of spending the summer in the desert.'

In the first frenzy of enthusiasm congratulations were showered down upon the two 'dickey-birds'. When some degree of calm had been restored, Andrés was left alone with the two champions.

'How are you feeling?' he asked them.

'Fine.'

'Do your wounds hurt much?'

'Yes.'

Their knees and elbows were entirely hidden in layers of sticking-plaster and bandages.

'But you are really pleased, aren't you?' insisted little Andrés.

'Yes, of course we're pleased,' replied the elder brother.

'I'm glad. Now you know what martyrdom is like. It's a mixture of physical pain and spiritual light. A

defeat converted into a victory. Now do you understand why you feel so pleased, though nearly every
part of your body hurts as if you'd had a thorough
beating?'

'So we have,' said the smaller boy.

'But you don't care,' went on Andrés, warming to
his subject. 'Saint Sebastian felt the same—exactly
the same—when he was pierced by arrows. Although
blood was gushing from his wounds he looked at the
sky and smiled.'

The 'Jackals of Mondoñedo' looked at the sky and
smiled.

'And you understand now about the rotten flesh? If
there's happiness in your heart it doesn't matter if
your flesh is beaten and torn. When I saw you were
brave enough to tackle that beast Manolo Ordóñez I
thought of Saint George defying the dragon. What
you've done to defend the colours of the Fourth,
which after all you don't greatly care about, surely
you can do to defend Christianity against a cannibal
tribe?'

The 'dickey-birds' did not reply. In their view the
question was superfluous. It seemed almost as if
Andrés had forgotten that he was talking to martyrs.

Javier came up to them. He was glowing. His face,
although a little swollen, had a certain resemblance to
that of Benvenuto Cellini's young Perseus, holding up
the head of Medusa.

'Well done, "dickey-birds",' he exclaimed, clapping the heroes on the back enthusiastically. 'You are a pair of tuskers!'

The 'dickey-birds' could not find words with which to respond to this inspiring epithet.

'Now we must put you in the junior eleven.'

'No. They aren't going to play any more,' said Andrés. 'This was just a trial of strength.'

'Well, that's just what I'm saying. Now anyone can see they're full of pluck!'

'You don't understand,' interrupted Andrés somewhat impatiently. 'I'm talking about quite a different kind of strength and a different kind of pluck.'

'What do you say to all this?' asked Javier, looking at the two brothers in amazement.

'That this is a question of a different kind of strength and a different kind of pluck,' declared the 'dickey-birds' one after the other, using Andrés's very words.

'The devil only knows what you're all talking about!'

'He will, you may be quite sure.'

Other boys now came up to congratulate the 'dickey-birds' and the conversation came to an end.

Andrés went to look for Regina to thank her for her moral support, but he could not find her. The little girl had run home, in answer to a summons to go to her father, who had been taken suddenly worse. But this Andrés did not know until the following day.

As it began to get dark, Javier and Andrés walked together to the now deserted football field. They had been given the job of taking down the poles from which hung the school flag, and other decorations put up for the occasion. As they carried out their task Javier asked Andrés a question which had been bothering him ever since that morning, but so much had been happening that he had had no time to formulate it.

'What was that you said about that dog on the Island?'

'D'you mean Gris?'

'Yes. You said he was a hundred years old or some such nonsense.'

'Certainly I said he was a hundred years old; but it isn't nonsense at all. Gris was a mysterious dog who was always to be seen at the side of Don Bosco at the most critical moments. He was with the Saint when he had to return by night through dangerous regions, like the Island, and he used to defend him whenever anyone attacked him. I'm sure ours was the same Gris.'

'How could it be? The only animal that lives so long is a carp. Not dogs. How can you believe a dog has been alive for a century?'

'It's easier to believe that a mysterious dog has been alive for a century than that a perfectly ordinary dog that doesn't know us runs to meet us wagging his tail. Nothing is impossible for a mysterious dog.'

There was a short silence during which Javier reflected that it was a great pity that such a friendly boy as Andrés, and so good at selecting football players too, should have such lapses from sanity.

'You know quite well I don't believe in miracles,' he said at last. 'It all seems ridiculous to me.'

'I know,' replied Andrés. 'You're like the flies. Flies don't believe in miracles either.'

'Look here! If you call me a fly I'll knock you down!'

Javier had very little patience. He was in fact famous in the school for his quick temper. Anyone who saw him now, as he raised one of the poles he had just pulled up and threatened little Andrés with it, would have advised the latter to run for his life. But Andrés was very stubborn, and he did not budge.

'You are a fly, and worse than a fly,' he repeated obstinately. 'If you think you have the right to laugh at miracles, I have the right to laugh at flies.'

The pole in Javier's hands swept through the air, and was just going to land on little Andrés's head when they both heard a menacing bark.

'Who barked?' asked Javier, ashy-pale.

'A dog. You don't suppose it was a fly, do you?'

The two boys looked at each other in silence for several seconds.

'I would have broken your head open if I hadn't remembered in time that you're smaller than me.'

'I knew you would remember in time. Otherwise, I would have run away,' said little Andrés very calmly. And they quietly went on with their work.

XVI

WHEN Regina got a message that she must go home to her father, as he was very ill, she began to run blindly back along the shore. The roaring of the sea seemed to come from her own breast, and the sky looked black as night though it was still day. For the first time in her life she was torn by the agony of feeling herself to blame. Why had she left him all alone? Why had she left him to die among strangers, while she went off to amuse herself? Yet that morning had not begun any worse than other days, and he had even enjoyed his breakfast. She had thought him better, because he didn't use foul language nor seem in a bad temper, but was rather easy-going. How long the way seemed across the beach to her house! She would never get there. Her mouth felt dry with a burning thirst.

When she got to her own part of the town, everyone who saw her knew why she was running so fast with terror in her eyes.

'It's Dimas's daughter. I hope she finds him alive!'

'Be quick, girl, he's sinking fast!'

'Make haste, if you want to get his blessing!'

The child ran on without pausing, almost without drawing breath, with the taste of blood in her mouth and lips parched with thirst, drenched in cold sweat. She could hardly recognize the women who spoke to her. She did not know who they were. Surely she had never seen those faces before? It was the voice of Death which was ringing in her ears, which seemed to come to her from every side. In the doorway of her house a group of neighbours stood waiting for her. The widow Sandrach was officiously in control of the situation, and had gone so far as to start a collection for the funeral expenses without waiting for the poor man to die. It was she who tearfully embraced Regina, and, with an arm still around her, took her up to her father's room.

Poor Dimas had grown so thin lately that his body scarcely humped the coverlet. When Regina came in, the dying man's dull eyes fastened for a moment upon his daughter's face, and he said something inaudible.

'She doesn't understand,' said one of the neighbours.

'He's been like that for quite a while, and no one knows what he wants.'

'He's thirsty,' said Regina, and she brought the sick man a glass of water.

Dimas drank a few sips eagerly, and Regina noticed that as he did so her own thirst seemed to be relieved.

Then Dimas leaned back on his pillows and closed his eyes. The doctor and the priest both arrived together. The neighbours knelt while Extreme Unction was administered to the dying man. Regina, pale and wide-eyed, could not weep, but the salt taste of tears was in her mouth.

The doctor could do no more than confirm what everyone knew. The unfortunate man might die at any moment. His heart was giving out. After patting the shoulders of the little girl and the widow Sandrach, whom he took for a relation, he went away.

Several minutes passed. Nothing was heard but the feeble rattle of the dying man's breath, and, far off, the roar of the sea. Suddenly Dimas opened his eyes, looked at his daughter and said one word:

'*Chica.*'

This was what he had called Regina when she was small, when peace and comfort reigned in that house. The name *Chica* evoked the old days of prosperity and happiness in her mother's lifetime.

A great sob shook the breast of the little girl. The neighbours looked at each other complacently because they saw that the little girl was suffering as God meant her to.

Regina came close to the bed and embraced her father, lifting him from the bed as she put both arms round his fragile shoulders, and pressing him to her breast.

'Father! Father! my darling!' she cried, while the head of poor Dimas who was already dead lay on his daughter's shoulder like the head of a sleeping child.

XVII

A FEW days later, little Andrés was unexpectedly sent for during the break. Someone was waiting to see him in the visitors' room. It was several months since the boy had seen his uncle, and when he saw him now, tall and thin, standing at the far end of the room, he thought how much he had aged.

They sat down opposite each other, and Alejo Vidal began talking in rather an uneasy manner. Andrés listened as if in a dream, without paying much attention.

Alejo Vidal was one of those men who feel humiliated to admit that they are short of money. As a result, he found it easier to go short of some of the necessaries of life than to face the embarrassment of giving a servant too small a tip. Accustomed to hearing himself praised for his generosity to his sister's son, it went very much against the grain to have to make the announcement that he was now practically penniless, and could not any longer undertake the expense of the boy's education.

As he talked his cheeks flushed and his voice grew gruff. But he still had not hit upon the exact phrase and the best words in which to inform his nephew that he was a ruined man. He took a thin, darned handkerchief from his pocket and began to polish his spectacles. Now that he saw the boy's face blurred by his own myopia, he found it easier to come to the point.

'Then just lately some transactions I was engaged in turned out very unluckily . . . I don't know whether at your age you understand this sort of thing . . .'

Andrés hardly heard what he was saying; he was sunk in limitless boredom.

'Yes, Uncle, I understand perfectly.'

Alejo went on talking. Sadly the boy remembered what an agreeable, good-looking and well-dressed man his uncle used to be, and saw him now, trying to hide his poverty behind his habitual air of sophistication.

The afternoon wore on. The visitors' room was invaded by shadows, bit by bit. Alejo Vidal's gold tooth flashed in the semi-darkness. Andrés felt more uncomfortable, more desperately bored every moment. To pass the time he began to work out imaginary chess moves on the tiles of the floor.

'At the moment,' said his uncle, bringing the tiresome conversation to a conclusion, 'at the moment, my dear Andrés, I simply must economize. It's only a question of a few months while I get my affairs back on to a sound footing. But for the present I find I must take you away from school. The fees are extremely high, and an industrious boy like you doesn't need such severe discipline. You can work on your own, be free . . .'

The word 'free' awoke Andrés from his wool-gathering. But he in no way connected it with his studies; he relished it for its own splendid succulent flavour. Free! Free! He saw all the roads in the wide world stretching before him, for him to choose which he liked. He felt that the whole earth belonged to him, as it did to tramps and pilgrims. Free!

He looked Alejo Vidal in the face, and said simply: 'Thank you, Uncle. Thank you very much.'

Half an hour later, when Alejo Vidal left the school, Andrés went down to the beach, without bothering to get leave.

In the distance he saw Regina sitting on a rock. She was dressed in mourning, as she had been when he first saw her, and looked thin and fragile in her badly-dyed black dress, tinged with green by the evening light. He went up to her with eyes shining with happiness, and said:

'I'm poor, Regina. I'm as poor as the shepherd waiting for dawn on the mountains; poor as St.

Francis, poor as Carlota Pelín the sylph lying on the steps of the Bernardine convent. There's nothing to hold me back. I'm free. Do you know what that means, Regina?'

The little girl stared back at him. She too was poor. Did that mean she was free?

The beach was deserted. And it was nearly dark. The full moon had risen above the horizon and the shadows of the two children on their high rock were outlined upon the sea; they seemed small, infinitely small, against the vastness of the earth and under the vastness of the moonlit sky.

'Come on,' said little Andrés.

And Regina got up and walked beside him.

Innumerable shells, thrown up by the mysterious sea, crunched under their feet, but they did not stoop to pick them up. The cool sea foam washed their bare toes.

'Where are we going?' Regina asked.

'To the other side of the world, to Asia, to convert the heathen.'

FINIS